With his first incon
any formal system
is necessarily incom
this result to physic.
nite set of laws (i.e. axioms) that will explain everything
(i.e. hoping to find a complete formal system capable of
pressing everything). In practice, we continually find
phenomena that cannot be explained by our existi
alone — requiring the addition of at least one mo
explain what we have observed. We imagine tha
we will finally reach the end of this process and posse
complete formal theory of everything, but incompleteness
tells us that this process is unending and that we will always
need to increase the number of laws to account for all the
phenomena the universe contains.

What is needed is a theoretical framework that describes
the process of how physical laws are created, such that an
n+1th law can always be incorporated without breaking
consistency with those laws that have already been established. This I have achieved. In the process, I have unified
special relativity with quantum mechanics, providing an
explanation of entanglement without relying on hidden
variables or faster-than-light travel, and of why superposition is observed as a consequence of entanglement.

ON REALITY

A UNIFICATION OF SPECIAL RELATIVITY AND QUANTUM MECHANICS

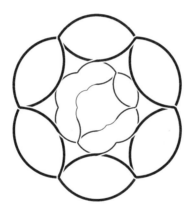

MORGAN JONES

Set in 11 pt EB Garamond
Typeset by Morgan Jones
Cover art by Morgan Jones

Printed by: Copytech (UK) Limited trading as
Printondemand-worldwide.com, 9 Culley Court, Bakewell Road,
Orton Southgate, Peterborough, PE2 6XD

ISBN: 978-1-7393685-0-0

lamppo.st

Dedicated to Pope Paul III

Contents

Preface

Why do we observe phenomena that necessitate indeterminacy prior to observation? *Why* don't we notice quantum phenomena at scales similar to our own? *How* can we intuitively understand entanglement without hidden variables or faster-than-light communication?

These questions have gone unanswered since their inception a century ago, but their solutions are provided by a simple extension of Einstein's theory of special relativity. This solution, named *relational quantum mechanics*, has been outlined in the chapters 'RELATIONAL QUANTUM MECHANICS' and 'SUPERPOSITION IS ENTANGLEMENT'. An interpretation of this theory, and its implications for our understanding of the universe and of our selves, is discussed in the remaining chapters 'INTERPRETATION' and 'ZEN'.

The theories contained herein are all original, in that they originated from my own thought, and unoriginal, in that I am not the first to conceive of them. Here I have written of them in language consistent with those who have written of them before me, so that this book does not deviate unnecessarily from the existing literature.

A number of grammatical quirks are present throughout the text where the content of my theories differ significantly from the metaphysical assumptions of the English language. Where I could conceive of a new parsable grammar, I have used it even if doing so breaks convention; where I could not, I have made use of footnotes to clarify my meaning.

I

Relational Quantum Mechanics

"Man is the measure of all things: of the things that are, that they are, of the things that are not, that they are not."

Protagoras

R*ELATIONAL QUANTUM MECHANICS* (RQM) was first described by Carlo Rovelli in 1994.

RQM throws away an unjustified assumption most physicists take with them to their work, and in doing so solves much of the vaguery present in our conventional understanding of quantum mechanics; it throws away the assumption of an *absolute*, or *observer-independent*, state of a system and replaces it with a *relational, observer-dependent*, state of a system. The justification for this change of assumption is that it better describes the universe we observe experimentally, in which we never actually observe objects, we only observe our observations of them.

Discarding the assumption of an observer-independent universe is in-line with the history of scientific progress. Kepler, Copernicus, and Galileo threw away the assumption of geocentrism and replaced it with heliocentrism. Shapley and Hubble threw away heliocentrism and replaced it with galactocentrism. Hubble then threw away galactocentrism and replaced it with acentrism (where *a* is the Greek prefix meaning *none*). Einstein supported the acentricity of the universe with his theory of special relativity, in which he rejected observer-independent measurements of velocity and consequently the notions of simultaneity and linear time. *RQM* expands Einstein's theory by rejecting any and all observer-independent observations of a system.

Suppose that we are an observer of a system with a quality

we wish to measure. To help us visualise such a setting, imagine a cone placed on the ground, and yourself and a friend to be stood some distance away from it. You may remark "the cone is two metres away", and your friend may remark "the cone is three metres away". Who is right?

We intuitively understand that the answer to this question is relative. It is possible for you to be two metres from the cone, and for your friend to be three metres from it. The fact that you measure different qualities doesn't mean that one of you is right and the other is wrong. The quality of distance does not exist locally in the cone, but instead exists as a relation between yourself and the cone — between the observer and the system.

RQM states that all qualities of a system observed by an observer belong not to the system, but to the relation between observer and system. It is therefore possible for a second observer to make a different yet consistent observation of the system.

The implications of this are simultaneously broad and insignificant. On the one hand, nothing changes: our conventional understanding of quantum mechanics still applies from the perspective of a given observer as the observer still experiences events that can be described by the collapse of a wave function. On the other hand, relational quantum mechanics no longer requires a realist universe; no statement is true absolutely, it is only true from the perspective of a given observer.

RQM makes one further assumption. Traditional physics proposes that there is a difference between macroscopic and microscopic physics — in which macroscopic things are explained by classical physics and microscopic things are explained by a distinct set of laws known as quantum physics. The distinction between macro and micro occurs at some unspecified and inexact hazy boundary between the two. *RQM* does away with this distinction and instead states that the principles that govern macroscopic systems are the same as those that govern microscopic systems. As a consequence, we expect to see quantum phenomena take place at all scales.

We summarise our principles as follows:[1]

Principle 1. *All qualities of a system do not belong to a system but to the relation between an observer and the system. As a consequence, no statement is true absolutely, but instead is true relative to an observer.*

Principle 2. *An observer will see the world around them to be logically consistent.*[2]

Principle 3. *We make no distinction between the principles that govern macroscopic and microscopic systems.*

---

[1] Note that these principles aren't laws, they are closer in nature to observations. As such, they are fallible and subject to change. Nonetheless, they are the best we currently have, and we can still reason from them to gain a greater understanding of the universe.

[2] As an exercise for the reader, what does *Gödel's first incompleteness theorem* say about a system that is consistent? And why might *Gödel's second incompleteness theorem* prevent us from providing a proof for the consistency we assume?

2

Superposition is Entanglement

"What is true for you is true for you, and what is true for me is true for me."

Protagoras

L ET'S INVESTIGATE an edge case.[1] Take a spin-zero particle and decay it into a pair of spin-$\frac{1}{2}$ particles. By the conservation of angular momentum, the total spin before and after the decay must be zero; hence whenever one particle is observed to be spin *up* on some axis, the

---

[1]By the end of this chapter we will see that it is not an edge case; it is the fundamental phenomenon that underlies all observations.

7

other is always found to be spin *down* on that same axis so that the two spins sum to zero. Even though we have made one *up* and one *down* particle, which particle is which will not be determined until an observation is made. In the view of *RQM*, this observation must be made from the perspective of an observer, and the measured quality will belong to the relation between the particle and the observer. We disallow hidden variable theories (which have already been disproved by observed violations of Bell's inequality) as they propose the particle to have absolute values which belong to it rather than its relation to an observer. Hence, from the perspective of an observer, it is truly indeterminate whether a particle is *up* or *down* prior to observation.

We separate the particles by some large distance,[2] and dispatch Alice and Bob to make observations of one particle each. From Alice's perspective, she measures her particle to be either *up* or *down* and, within a microsecond of her observation, Bob observes his particle to be either

---

[2] There is no theoretical upper limit on this distance. In 2017, a distance of over 1200km was achieved from the Micius satellite to bases in Lijian, Yunnan and Delingha, Quinhai.

up or *down*.[3] Alice and Bob record their results, and then travel towards each other to compare them.

Every time we repeat this experiment, we observe one particle to be *up* and the other *down*. It was not possible for the particles to communicate, since to do so would require they share information faster-than-light, and it was not possible for the particles to have known whether they were *up* or *down* prior to their separation, since their spin is a quality of their relation to an observer they have yet to interact with. How then is it possible that we always observe one particle to be *up* and the other to be *down*?

By Principle 1 of the previous chapter, when Alice measured her particle, no absolute quality of the particle was measured; instead, a quality of the relation between Alice and her particle was measured. Alice and Bob then meet up. By Principle 3, Alice observing Bob is also a quantum event. By Principle 2, the outcome of this

---

[3]From the perspective of Bob, he measures his particle to be either *up* or *down* and, within a microsecond of his observation, Alice observes her particle to be either *up* or *down*. The disagreement about the order of events is the result of special relativity.

quantum event must be consistent with Alice's previous observations. Therefore, if Alice observes her particle to be *up*, Alice must observe Bob's observations of his particle as being *down* so that conservation of angular momentum is satisfied from the perspective of Alice. Since Alice and Bob travel towards each other at less than the speed of light, no information must travel faster-than-light.

The implication of this interpretation is that both Alice and Bob may observe *up*, but when they meet, both will observe the other as having seen *down*. This can be thought of as a superposition of possibilities. Since, by Principle 1, no absolute reality exists (only a relational one), and in this example only two consistent (Principle 2) realities are possible from Alice's perspective (Alice observes *up* and Alice observes Bob as observing *down* or Alice observes *down* and Alice observes Bob as observing *up*), when Alice makes her observation of her particle, the wave function collapses from her perspective, deciding which of the two possibilities she inhabits. Her future observations of Bob are then consistent with her previous observations of her particle, as the wave function has already collapsed from her perspective. Both Alice and Bob are themselves a part of the quantum event, which we expect by Principle 3.

Whilst it may seem strange that Alice and Bob can inhabit separate consistent accounts, this interpretation violates no observed phenomena and explains at least one unexplained phenomenon. As such, it provides a better description of physics than does a realist account, which bases its belief system on the idea that there is one privileged perspective that all other observers within the universe must themselves make observations consistent with, despite the fact that no evidence for this privileged perspective has ever surfaced.

It is also worth noting that this explanation of quantum entanglement explains why we observe quantum super-positions in the first place, and why we don't notice quantum superpositions at scales nearing humanity (i.e. of objects much larger than atoms).

If I plan to observe the spin of a single particle to be either *up* or *down* on some axis, then, prior to my obser-vation, the value of its spin exists in a superposition of *up* and *down* (with their associated probabilities described by a wave function). Once I make my observation, it appears as though the particle permanently takes on a defined value, i.e. if our friend Carol were later to observe the same particle, they'd make the same reading as us.

However, this is again a quantum entanglement between ourselves, the particle, and Carol. It isn't the case that the particle now takes on a fixed value; instead, the relationship between us and the particle has a fixed value, and when Carol later observes it, our observation of Carol's observation must be consistent with what we've already observed. Hence, before our first observation, any value is possible, but once the wave function collapses (from our perspective) we will perceive every subsequent event as consistent with our measured value (i.e. it will appear as though a fixed value belongs to the particle).

Since we routinely observe the values of things that are human-scale, we rarely notice the quantum entanglement present in our daily-lives as everything must appear to be consistent with what we've already observed. The reason really tiny things can appear to exist in superpositions is exactly because we've made no previous observations that constrain the outcome of our observations of them. This does not mean that quantum events don't take place on the scale of atoms or larger, instead it is the case that we don't notice them.

3

Interpretation

"It is bright and spotless as the void, having no form or appearance whatever. To make use of your minds to think conceptually is to leave the substance and attach yourselves to form."

Huángbò

A S A RESULT of these mechanics, we do not have a universe in which pre-existing objects determine the future through a chain of cause-and-effect; we instead have a universe of relations whose ends coalesce to form the objects with which we are familiar, and our observations of which are constrained by the principle of consistency.

If we imagine a particle alone in a void, it does not make sense to speak of it as having *mass*. It is only by introducing a second particle to which it relates (via an interaction we term *gravity*) that *mass* takes any meaning. All a particle's qualities can be assessed in this way; *mass*, *charge*, *spin*, *colour* etc. All are relations.

In what sense, then, does the particle exist given that it possesses no quality, quantity, or description that belongs to itself? The answer is that it doesn't, it is *empty* — only the relations exist, and where the end points of relations coalesce in spacetime we can interpret the existence of an object at that location. The relations exist, the object is illusory.

A web of relations is thus woven through spacetime;[1] carrying in its wake every implicit object in the universe. Our place in the universe restricts our view, allowing us only to see those relations that are connected to us radially.

---

[1] In this context it does not make sense to distinguish past, present, and future. As such, my use of the past participle 'woven' is a poetic choice taken due to the limitations of the English language rather than an assertion that all of spacetime has already been written.

A naïve reading of this theory favours *solipsism*, however such an interpretation neglects that integral to the theory's formulation is the principle of *acentricity* — that the universe is composed of relations precisely because there is no one true perspective — and so it would be foolish to suddenly decide our perspective is the only such one. This does, of course, require an element of faith. I cannot empirically verify the existence of other view points, and so my belief that they exist is an act of cosmic humility rather than a scientific fact.

Such humility provides a stronger foundation for a belief in God than does a realist interpretation. God cannot noticeably intervene in our affairs, since any such intervention would be reinterpreted by us for consistency, but she can hold the web of fragmented-reality together. In such an interpretation, God may be both omniscient and omnipresent but can no longer be omnipotent, since in an established universe the ultimate power of interpretation lies with each observer.

In this way, the supposed paradox of an unstoppable force meeting an immovable object is solved. From the perspective of the object, it is immovable first and so the force will be interpreted as stoppable for consistency; from the perspective of the force, it will consider itself to be unstoppable first and so the object will be interpreted to be movable for consistency. Each of the force and the object exists within its own consistent account, and yet the union of these perspectives creates a contradiction.

A result of this is that, given the consistency principle, the order of events matters to our perception of reality.[2] Events that occur first are given greater precedence than those which follow them, as the consistency principle requires future events be consistent with those which have already occurred.

Since the theory of special relativity proposes that each of us experiences a different ordering of events, each of us will inhabit a different perception of reality as constrained by the consistency principle. Each perception is internally consistent yet may conflict with the perception of another; no person can possess a complete description of the universe since it would require the union of contradictory perspectives.

---

[2] This ordering of events solves *Buridan's ass* without requiring the notion of *free will*.

What, then, are the laws of physics?

If a mass does not exist absolutely, but instead only in relation to another mass, where in the interaction does the law of gravity exist? It doesn't, it is *empty*. The relations exist, the law is illusory. Instead, our perception of gravity, and our requirement that mass act consistently with it, is a consequence of the *anthropic principle*.

If gravity did not exist, then it would not have been possible for human life to form; we perceive that human life exists, therefore we perceive that gravity exists. But this gravity isn't actually located anywhere, except as is required by the consistency principle. Gravity must exist for us to exist, so we must perceive gravity to exist for consistency with our prior perception that we ourselves exist. All our physical laws exist in this way, embedded in each relation by the principle of consistency.

Because of this, the physical law need not exist prior to our observation of it. Laws themselves exist in superposition prior to observation, and remain fixed afterwards only for consistency. But since we exist, any physical law must only take a value that is consistent with our existence. As such, the nature of the entire cosmos is in flux to become consistent with what must've been for our own existence to take place.

And we know that we exist — or rather, I know that I exist. It is the only thing of which a person can be certain. Think on that for a moment, then think about the fact that you're thinking, then if you're thinking, you must exist. This *first principle* was summarised by René Descartes as *'cogito, ergo sum'* (common translation: *'I think, therefore I am'*).

Since our own existence is necessary for us to make further observations, it takes first precedence in our order of events — preceding every event we have since observed. This *first event* then constrains every event that follows it via the principle of consistency. Everything that is or ever has been must be observed by you to be consistent with the existence in the here-and-now of yourself as an observer, else it wouldn't be true that you are observing. This *first event* precedes even your observations of the past, since your observations of all things in the universe are constrained by the speed of light such that you only ever observe things that have already occurred, and yet for you to be observing the past you must first exist, meaning that in your ordering of events the past occurs after your present existence; you exist even before time itself, and the past is not fixed but is instead in flux to become consistent with the here-and-now existence of your self.

4
Zen

"To study the buddha way is to study the self. To study the self is to forget the self. To forget the self is to be actualized by myriad things. When actualized by myriad things, your body and mind as well as the bodies and minds of others drop away. No trace of realization remains, and this no-trace continues endlessly."

Dōgen

BUT IS the here-and-now existence of yourself as an observer *truth*? Certainly it is not truth from the perspective of another observer who may inhabit a contradictory reality that is consistent to themselves but not to you; a supreme truth must include the union of these disjoint and contradictory perspectives, but no such truth can be reached from the confines of any one observer.

In the pursuit of truth, it is then required of us that we reject the notion of individual perspective as such a perspective requires a distinction of 'self' and 'other' that gives rise to contradictions between our own and other perspectives (as occurred when both Alice and Bob observed *up*). Instead, we see that truth is rooted in nondualism — making no distinction between one's self and the rest of the universe.

Since our individual perspective is generated by extension on our *first event*, we reject Descartes' *first principle* to prevent this erroneous perspective from rooting itself in our minds, and in so doing thwart the sequence of events that arise as a consequence of it. Our position in spacetime is thus *empty*, as it is only the result of the relations connected to it and so possesses no essence that is self-contained, nor any relation to itself such that it can exist distinct from the rest of the universe.[1] Our percep-

---

[1]A self-referential relation of one's self to one's self is the root of sentience as it grounds perspective via an analog to the statement 'I

tion of reality ceases, since no event is observed, and our actions as perceived by others continue only insofar as they are events from their perspective.

This is the essence of *Buddha-nature* — of being without being. It is present in all things, from the smallest pebble to the mightiest king. The error of sentient beings lies in their capacity to view the universe dualistically; we may think of a pebble as making no such error, and so as already having realised their nature as Buddha.[2]

Since any attempt to formalise an understanding of the universe requires we experience the *first event* of identifying with ourselves as a basis for future dualistic observations, no such attempt to understand the universe is made by an enlightened being. As such, the reasoning that has brought us to this understanding of the universe is not present in the mind of a buddha, but is instead akin to a *raft* that we may use to cross a river and of which we dispose once the river has been crossed.

---

think therefore I am'.

   [2] It may entertain the reader to know that my first encounter with this concept was when, as a child, I noted how happy I would be as a carrot — existing as a part of the universe without conception of it.

The raft we have produced through our study of quantum mechanics is alike in construction to the rafts of *kōans* used to achieve the same end. The famous kōan *'what is the sound of one hand clapping?'* achieves this aim by first posing an impossible question, and then implicitly tasking us with noting that we can answer it if we accept that clapping is a *relation* between *two* hands, and so to consider the question from the perspective of only *one* hand is to place into false duality one hand with the other, when in fact both exist in a single nondualistic whole. In short, the question cannot be answered when the student engages in dualism, and once the student recognises nondualism as true, no answer need be sought as the *raft* has served its purpose of crossing the river of dualistic thinking that prevents the student from realising their Buddha-nature.

There may exist concern that Buddhism fails to provide any ethical guidance to its followers, since to define 'right' and 'wrong' would be to place 'right' and 'wrong' into a false duality. The question arises: could a buddha commit murder?

Consider an act you believe to be reprehensible — assault, rape, theft, etc. All such immoral acts have in common that they are one person causing harm to another for personal gain, but this requires the offender to have in their mind a duality between themselves and the victim; without this duality, there can be no motivation for the immoral act, and so the immoral act does not occur.

If a sentient being wishes to know whether a buddha would act in such-and-such a way towards a person, they need only ask themselves the *golden rule* of whether they would wish to be treated in the same way; since a buddha perceives no distinction between 'self' and 'other', they could not act towards an other in any way that they would not act towards their self.

This mode of thinking incurs a problem though. Relying on the golden rule as an approximation of Buddhist *right action* reinforces the false duality between 'self' and 'other' as it asks us to *'do unto others as you would have them do unto you'*. This false duality is the very source of immoral acts, since it is by considering one's self as able to gain by the deprivation of another that the possibility for immoral action arises. Hence, focus on *right action* in terms of 'self' and 'other' may end up having the opposite effect of causing immoral action.

This effect is exemplified by the frequency with which priests commit sexual immorality with children. A priest has a strong belief in how they ought to act towards others, and this belief reinforces the distinction between 'self' and 'other' that is required for the very immoral acts they attempt to avoid.

In the Christian tradition, Jesus, being God, could not be tempted to transgress God, since to do so would be to harm himself. Unless a Christian accepts, as Jesus did, that there is no distinction between themselves and God, and by extension between themselves and the rest of the universe, they will continue to reinforce the division between 'self' and 'other' that it required for their transgressions. It is for this reason that Adam and Eve's consumption of fruit from the *tree of the knowledge of good and evil* separated them from God, cementing them as mortal subjects of the universe — their knowledge of good and evil forcing them into a duality in which they themselves existed distinct from God and so kicking into motion the chain of events that follow from their *first event*, famously their *second event* being their observation that they were naked, and a later event being their own deaths. As such, our *first event* is synonymous with *original sin*, and it is only by rejection of this *first event* that true knowledge of the universe and an escape from death becomes possible.

We see by this that the thread of truth present in Buddhism is not wholly absent from the Abrahamic religions. The compatibilities of Buddhism with Hinduism and Taoism follows by direct descent — with Hinduism being the religion of the Buddha and his family prior to his enlightenment circa the 6th century BCE, and Taoism being the first religion of many in the Chinese school of Chan Buddhism from which Zen split in the 13th century CE, the split occurring only due to the geographical distance between China and Japan and not due to any difference in ideology or practice.

It would be difficult for me to conclude this book without addressing Aristotle's (384 BCE - 322 BCE) influence on the Western canon; his most significant contribution being that he was the first person to formalise a system of logic. It appears obvious to the modern reader that a statement such as 'I see a red lamppost' is either true or false, but this was not obvious to a reader before Aristotle, nor should it be obvious to you.

To state something is 'true or false' is to place into a duality the state of being 'true' or 'false'. The universe laughs at our attempts to define such dualities, instead placing all things into superposition prior to observation. Since observation depends inherently upon the duality of 'self' and 'other', the state of a thing being 'true' or 'false' after our observation is not a property of the universe but instead a duality inherited from the act of observation. To reason that you can observe something to be 'true' or 'false' is to reason cyclically, because implicit in your observation is the duality which you then observe. The universe does not contain such dualities; it is only by our imposition on it, reasoning from a flawed base, that we perceive them at all.

Postface

IT IS THE undesirable ideological consequences of this theory that will lead to its initial rejection, and its fundamental truth that will lead to its eventual acceptance.

Owing to its incompatibility with existing lines of enquiry, it is susceptible to many criticisms that will seem valid to those who hold their beliefs without critical thought. To such people, dogma appears self-evident and so is never questioned; you cannot reason against such a person since it was not by reason that they reached their convictions. To these people, I say that it is more ludicrous to hold the belief in an objective reality that exists beyond the corruption of our senses whilst our sense-perceptions form the only basis on which we have knowledge of that reality, than it is to accept all truths as being relative to an observer.

I admit that I too may be guilty of reasoning from dogma, since dogma is the very thing that seems so essential that it evades any motivation by us to question it, and as such I am unable to recognise all those things I ought to question. Nonetheless, the kōan constructed in the form of RQM provides us with enough truth that we may realise our Buddha-nature, and it is by this metric that I am satisfied with the content of this work.

This metric will not be satisfactory to most scientists, who will instead view it as the act of me dismissing any potential criticism, since no criticism could falsify the existence of Buddha-nature that only takes place without observation. To this person, I state that the assumption that one day we will discover a new phenomenon that explains quantum entanglement within the framework of an objective science is itself unfalsifiable, since the future cannot be observed. As such, all science motivates itself by unfalsifiable assumptions; I prefer the assumptions that presently provide a rational interpretation of quantum mechanics to the assumptions that suggests a rational interpretation exists only in an inaccessible future — akin to a destined messiah that never arrives — and so refuses to question itself in the meantime.

It will be important to the reader's understanding of the text that it was not with Buddhism in mind that I set upon writing, nor was it the case until the final month of many years of inquiry that it became my goal. Initially, this book was a work of fiction to which the chapters that are now titled 'RELATIONAL QUANTUM MECHANICS' and 'SUPERPOSITION IS ENTANGLEMENT' were included as an appendix. It became clear to me that my motivation for writing existed wholly in this appendix, and so I abandoned the fictional element to focus solely on the consequences of the theory I had developed. Since this theory posed a contradiction of perspectives, I had to reject perspectives, which could only be achieved by rejecting the *first event* that grounds perspective. In doing so, an assertion of non-self is made as the barrier between 'self' and 'other' as a duality is broken, and it was on this basis that I noted similarities with Buddhism as I understood it from my studies many years prior.

I arrived at the theory of *RQM* in much the same way;

I didn't have the destination in mind, I simply kept asking myself how the phenomena I observed could be possible. Having already read Einstein, it seemed natural to take his theory of special relativity to its logical conclusion and treat all observed properties as relative; this then synced up nicely with the fact that observations of a quantum system are observer-dependent. The whole theory followed from this simple premise. By chance, I later came across the work of Carlo Rovelli, which was greatly refreshing as I had been feeling quite mad at the thought I may be alone in what seemed to me as a fairly obvious set of conclusions. I then adapted my written work to be consistent with Rovelli's, such that I did not need to coin any new terms or phrases.

It is not only to Rovelli I owe my thanks. To Douglas Hofstadter and Robert Pirsig I owe thanks for showing me it was possible to reach reasonable conclusions outside the prevailing dogma of our time. To Einstein and Gödel I owe thanks for showing me that one can reason something so obvious that it is a mystery it was not already widely known. To my husband George I owe so much, not least of which is the way he fostered my philosophical curiosity that might otherwise have died before I had a chance to complete this work. To Plato I owe thanks that he recorded so much ancient philosophy that would otherwise have been lost, and to his student Aristotle I owe thanks that he formalised a system worthy of criticism. To Gautama Buddha I owe thanks that he was able to bring into popular knowledge that same nature I, some two thousand years later, was able to derive again; to Dōgen and Huángbò I owe thanks for the preservation of Gautama's teachings via unburdened texts, so that I may understand my own experiences in terms of them. To Descartes I owe thanks for demonstrating that no degree of skepticism is too severe that it cannot bear fruit. To Protagoras and Gorgias I owe thanks not only for their teachings on relativism, but for pissing Plato off enough that he bothered to record their arguments. To my friends George, Lauren, Isaac, and Josh, I am grateful for their feedback on early copies of the manuscript and for proofreading my final draft prior to publication; nonetheless, all errors are my own.

Note on the Cover

THE COVER displays a rendition of one of Ochiai's hard unknots. An unknot is, in essence, simply a circle. A hard unknot is a circle that, without breaking, has been tangled and twisted into a state that doesn't appear possible to untangle — in fact, to untangle such an unknot requires we increase the number of crossings between strands before we may reduce it back down to zero.

The concept of a circle that is hard to untangle possesses a poetic significance when compared to the ensō as used in Zen art. An ensō (literally "circular form") is also a circle, traditionally painted in a single brushstroke, that is used as a metaphor for Buddha-nature owing to a circle's simple and unburdened nature. A hard unknot thus represents the difficulty of a sentient being in recognising their own Buddha-nature, requiring that they increase the complexity of their understanding of the universe before they may simplify it, whilst recognising Buddha-nature as nonetheless being inherent in them. A reference to our *raft* parable may again be made; the method to untangle a hard unknot is not present in the final circle.

I chose the specific unknot, first described by Ochiai, because it possesses a nice symmetry. It has 6 crossings on its exterior (first rung), within which exist 4 crossings on its second rung, within which exist 3 crossings on the innermost (third) rung. Between any two crossings on a rung exists at most one crossing on the next-most interior rung, which is required for a simple geometric representation on a fractal grid. Of the other famous unknots I found with crossing number lower than 13, namely 'H', 'J', the 'Culprit', the 'Monster', and the 'Goeritz' unknot, none possessed this quality.

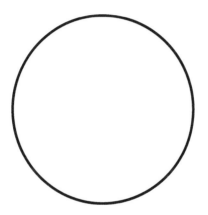